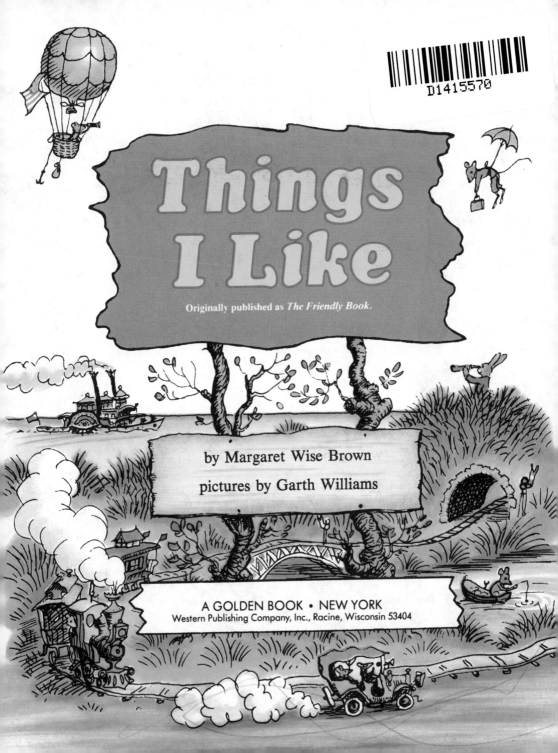

Things I Like

Originally published as *The Friendly Book*.

by Margaret Wise Brown

pictures by Garth Williams

A GOLDEN BOOK • NEW YORK
Western Publishing Company, Inc., Racine, Wisconsin 53404

I LIKE CARS
Red cars   Green cars
Sport limousine cars

I like cars
A car in a garage
A car with a load
A car with a flat tire
A car on the road
I like cars.

I LIKE TRAINS
Express trains
Toy trains
Streamline trains
Freight trains
Old trains
Milk trains

Any kind of train
A train in the station
Trains crossing the plains

Trains in a snowstorm
Trains in the rain
I like trains.

I LIKE STARS

Yellow stars
Green stars
Red stars
Blue stars
I like stars
Far stars
Quiet stars
Bright stars
Light stars
I like stars
A star that is shooting across the dark sky
A star that is shining right straight in your eye
I like stars.

I LIKE SNOW
Cold snow
Slow snow
White snow
Icy snow
I like snow
Snow falling softly with everything still
White in the blue night, white on the sill
White on the trees on the far distant hill
With everything still
I like snow.

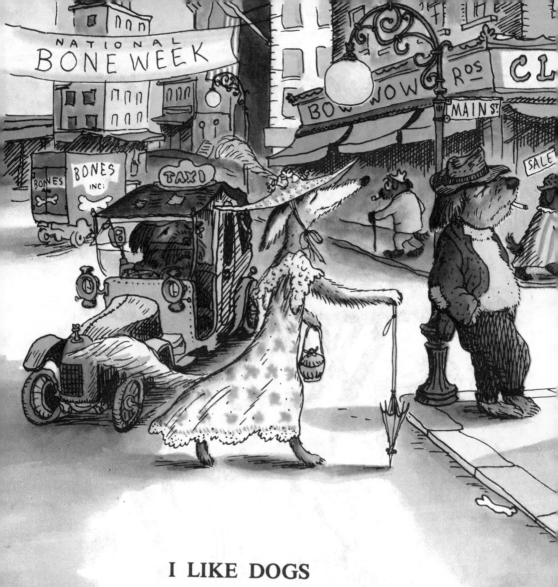

I LIKE DOGS
Big dogs   Little dogs
Fat dogs   Doggy dogs
Old dogs   Puppy dogs

I like dogs
A dog that is barking over the hill
A dog that is dreaming very still
A dog that is running wherever he will
I like dogs.

I LIKE BOATS

Any kind of boat
Tug boats   Tow boats
Large boats   Barge boats

Sail boats   Whale boats
Thin boats   Skin boats
Rubber boats   River boats
Flat boats   Cat boats
U boats   New boats

Tooting boats   Hooting boats
South American fruit boats
Bum boats   Gun boats
Slow boats   Row boats
I like boats.

I LIKE WHISTLES

Wild whistles   Bird whistles
Far-off heard whistles
Boat whistles   Train whistles
I like whistles

The postman's whistle
The policeman's whistle
The wind that blows away the thistle
Light as the little birds whistle and sing
And the little boy whistling in the spring
The wind that whistles through the trees
And blows the boats across the seas
I like whistles.

I LIKE PEOPLE
Glad people
Sad people
Slow people
Mad people
Big people
Little people

I like people.